GROWING
BOLD

HOW TO ENJOY LONG LIFE

GROWING
BOLD

HOW TO ENJOY LONG LIFE

MELANIE E. HARRINGTON

First Printing: 2016

ISBN 978-0-692-76372-8

Melanie E. Harrington
Post Office Box 454
Etna, CA 96027

www.melanieharrington.com

DEDICATION

To Papa

CONTENTS

I'm the perfect person to write this book about successful aging and planning ahead, because I never intended to do either. At the age of 16, my best friend and I hoped we would never make it to 40. At the age of 39, I told myself that 50 is the new 40. Now in my mid-50's, this thought dawns big and bright: *I, too, might get old.*

As part of the baby boomer generation, I knew the mantra, "Never trust anyone over 40". We were hip, cool, full of energy to change the world. We imagined getting older entailed the loss of those things we valued in ourselves and our peers. We did not yet know about the gifts.

A very small crack in my ageism started to appear during my 40's. I began to slowly figure out things about life that I had never known, things that made life saner and easier, and things that were so obvious as to make me embarrassed I'd never seen them before. My small accomplishments started to pile up, and I felt more secure in society. My failings and character flaws began to seem slightly less important.

My personal evolution was supported by my involvement in nursing home reform. In my early 30's, a new PhD with a coveted university position, I consulted to a lawyer on a case of nursing home abuse. I picked the jury and summarized medical and regulatory evidence for presentation in court. Our trial lasted five weeks, and the jury awarded a record (at that time) verdict of $95 million. The evidence we had collected supported the federal government's indictment of the nursing home chain for Medicare fraud. Our case championed the rights of elders in nursing homes, and I was bit. I became a full-time legal consultant, working to reform a broken system.

We sued nursing homes all over California, and even sued the State for failing to protect the residents. But after 12 years of relentless effort, nothing in the world of nursing homes changed. I embarked on a personal experiment to figure out how the broken nursing home model could actually be fixed. I became a Long-Term Care Ombudsman, advocating for elders in nursing homes and assisted living, but the bureaucratic program was too restrictive to permit any real reform. I became a nursing home administrator, attempting reforms from inside a troubled facility. But, despite my significant effort, and that of my dedicated staff, the actual lives of the elders remained largely the same.

I wrote a blog called "The Fine Art of Aging", that contained advice for elders living independently on how to avoid the nursing home. That information is useful, but I have increasingly seen that happy elders are those who have prepared themselves by long dedication to optimism, creativity, and other people.

For nearly 20 years, I have watched elders aging well and aging poorly, both in independent lives and inside the nursing home – as a legal consultant, an advocate, a nursing home manager, and as a daughter, granddaughter, and friend to elders I love.

Growing Bold is about the lessons I have learned in how to enjoy and value long life.

From the right vantage point, old age looks almost fun. For me, rejecting age denial is allowing me to dream about the future. Maybe I will become a painter! The more I think about the possibilities, the freer I feel. My 16-year-old self would be mortified.

~ Melanie E. Harrington

Welcome to Your Long Life

We have created bonus years for ourselves: 30 years of additional time compared to humans who came before us. Through sanitation and medication and operations, we have extended our time on the planet. The probability is that each of us will live for nearly 80 years, and the number living to 90 or more grows every year. We have tremendous opportunity to become the most experienced and fulfilled people who have ever lived.

But, have we focused so hard on the visionary feat of reaching the moon that we have given no thought to what we'll do when we get there?

Most of us avoid thinking about advanced age as long as we can. We permit our uncertainty, fear, and ageism to keep us from looking ahead. This culture-wide denial is epitomized in the frightening symbol of old age: the nursing home. The "rest home" oppresses its elderly residents and society at large by equating later years with institutionalization and disability.

The story of problem nursing homes is mainstream news. Greed-driven profit goals render elders mere commodities. There are inadequate numbers of staff to provide support, and poor quality supplies and food are obtained as cheaply as possible. These savings flow to unsympathetic corporate operators. Attempts by lawmakers and lawyers to reform this broken model create a nightmarish web of institutional rules that dictate every aspect of the elder's life.

But it is not just the reality of life in that institution that is so disturbing to us; it is the ageism, stereotyping, paternalism, and fear of mortality with which we have stamped this emblem of late life. We do not need to deform ourselves and our visions of age in this way.

The extra years of life we have attained have great value. Look around and see the meaningful achievements that are had in the bonus years. An artist may be at his height of creativity in "late works". Free time permits reading, learning a language, writing songs, starting a business, and more. For elders, now and in the future, there are magical gifts in age: a deepening relationship to the world, stronger connections to the past, and renewed liberty.

Even many elders relegated to nursing homes find meaning in their later years. They continue to engage life with good cheer, humor, and compassion. Imagine the courage and strength it takes to live well in that disheartening setting.

In every nursing home are nurses, nursing aides, cooks, and housekeepers who truly see the elderly people living there. The cook violates her budget to serve fresh strawberries. The activities director solicits donations to grow a garden. Nursing aides fight for the residents' rights. These people really get it, battling against strong countervailing forces to help the elders find moments of joy, freedom, and purpose.

It is high time we reject the idea that incarceration is a reasonable form of senior support. But, the necessary change will never be brought about by the industry, lawsuits, or regulations. It will only happen if we look ahead to our own futures and create something better.

> You never change things
> by fighting the existing
> reality. To change something,
> build a new model that makes
> the existing model obsolete.

R. Buckminster Fuller

There is no generation better equipped than the "Baby Boomers" to undertake this society-altering task of cultivating a love for later years. Coming of age in the 1960's and 70's taught us to question authority and demand cultural change. Maturing to middle age has given us perspective and the ability to laugh at our youthful selves. We are the ones poised to lead the charge. If we succeed, the nursing home model will have to change to adapt to us. We can do it – for ourselves, for our parents, and for future generations.

The time to start is now.

THE VALUE OF

CHARACTER

We dread the nursing home because we fear handing over our freedom to people who don't know us, corporations that see us as numbers, and caregivers who are shackled by a system that prevents them from helping us in the ways we want to be helped.

We dread giving up control, but in order to keep it we must take back the reins.

Preparing to age does not mean buying long-term care insurance or taking pills on time. It means becoming better aged versions of ourselves. For that, we have to turn inward. We have to seek out and learn new life skills.

Most importantly, we must begin to picture ourselves as happy, fulfilled elders.

What does that look like?

Where will the elder-you live?

How will the elder-you get the
support you may need to be happy?

How can you get ready to be an older,
better version of you?

Your answers are the root of the
future you will grow.

Nursing home residents, as a rule, are just as shocked as anyone else that they have grown old. They shake their heads in bewilderment at the 70, 80, 90 or more years that have rushed by so fast. They were not prepared.

Lesson One: Toughen Up

The challenge of growing old is daunting. Continuing losses of beloved people and animals. The body's progressive refusal to obey commands. The creative energy required to let go of old dreams and reinvest in the new.

There is tremendous value in the moments later years can bring, but they come at a cost. You must prepare yourself like a warrior training for battle. Keep a strong character, resolve to overcome enemies, and learn to laugh at yourself.

Trade in bitter protests for the fine art of gratitude.

A fascinating fact about nursing homes is that some people who live there are happy. Despite the rigid rules, lack of privacy, and conditions of institutional life, these people continue to appreciate and even enjoy being alive.

They have a knack for forging ahead bravely despite pain, disability and limitations. There is a real commitment to focusing on joy, and maintaining a strong allegiance to something outside themselves.

The longer you live, the greater your opportunities to count your blessings.

Consider two examples:

Henry:

Despite the stroke that confined him to a wheelchair and rendered his speech almost unintelligible, Henry enjoyed life. He watched ESPN 24/7 in his nursing home room, wore USC jerseys all the time, and yelled with excitement when his team won. Henry's enthusiasm was contagious and drew people to him. He was widely loved and often cited as an example of best practices in positive thinking.

Gladys:

A short-stay, rehabilitation patient, Gladys was at the nursing home to recover from a wrist fracture. She refused to engage in therapy because of pain, and she complained incessantly. Her constant misery was palpable and real, but how ungrateful did she appear to the other residents who were doing their best to be optimistic in the face of permanent disabilities?

Practice Self-Reliance

"Discontent is want of

self-reliance;

it is infirmity of will."

Ralph Waldo Emerson

In human nature, there is a constant balance between independence and symbiosis; avoiding overreliance takes frequent exercise of will. You do not wrest power away from institutional authorities by being overly dependent on them.

The first step in building a base for your fulfilled, older self is practicing self-determination. Then, if physical or mental declines come, you will seek out support on your own terms and only to the extent it is needed.

You will find it perfectly natural to remain an autonomous person.

There are people of all ages who suffer life in institutions through disability. Car wrecks, trauma, and medical conditions can cause physical injuries so severe that the victim is not able to live without 24-hour support. In general, these people are insistent on being as self-reliant as possible. They find it within themselves to continue to assert their personhood.

Practice Giving and Receiving Support

The idea is balance.

The goal is to be as self-reliant as possible, *within reason*.

Full enjoyment of bonus years may require gracious acceptance of some degree of physical or mental loss. This is the reality of long life. Giving support to elders in your life is a training ground for finding and keeping your balance.

There are elders in nursing homes who are so independent that they refuse to permit assistance at all. Their daily lives become battlegrounds. They are rude and abusive to the people kindly trying to help them.

But, being self-reliant doesn't mean you are a solitary creature surviving by your wits in a hostile world.

Mutual aid is why we live in groups.

THE VALUE OF

IDENTITY

So much can be lost as years go by, but it all leaves patches, scraps and mementoes. Successful aging demands a vigilant effort to continue seeing the pattern and building on what has been learned, done, lost, and loved.

See the fragile beauty in those minute stitches.

Strong identities are built up over time from repeated acts of self-respect and caring for others. You might be surprised how well they can withstand the sterile assault of nursing home walls or, even, dementia. It is possible to act like yourself even if you have forgotten your own name.

Build Allies

There is nothing so valuable in successful aging as friends. These are the people who know you, learn about your history, and share your values. Mutual affection and assistance create a climate where you feel supportive and supported, loving and loved.

Some people are lucky enough to have a best-friend spouse, partner, or relative. These beloved ones create a foundation for building a quality older version of you.

But beyond honored allies of time, there is value to forging relationships as you go. Life has a swift current at times, and even the largest boulders can end up downstream.

You can't replace foundational people who leave your life, but that is not the goal here: remaining part of the world is.

Practice recognizing potential allies. Invest time in seeing whether you guessed right. Cultivate the friendships you find there.

"In everyone's life, at some
time, our inner fire goes out.
It is then burst into flame by
an encounter with another
human being. We should all
be thankful for those people
who rekindle the inner
spirit."

Albert Schweitzer

Be a Whole Person

To see a person at a single slice of time prevents a view of the whole person. Each human being is a continuously growing collection of all the people he has ever been. The infant, adolescent, college kid, grandpa – the older he gets, the thicker the layers.

Every subsequent self contains all the earlier selves.

Every feature has its roots in a younger version.

To know someone is to see the layers, in appearance and in identity.

The meaning of your life is embedded in all those layers and they take up a lot of room. Fight for the space you need to be whole.

There is a temptation to see all nursing home residents superficially, as if they were all the same. But, this one was a fiery redhead who was crowned Miss Vermont at age 19. That one was a well-regarded dog trainer. The career nurse feels like she is always at work here. And the fishing boat captain has stories like you won't believe. They are people – whole people, too.

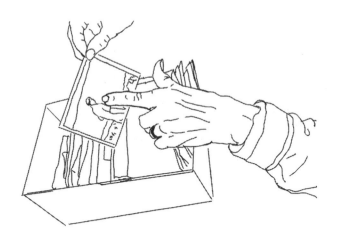

"Wrinkles should merely indicate where smiles have been."

Mark Twain

Revel in Uniqueness

"If I'm going to sing like

someone else,

then I don't need to

sing at all."

Billie Holiday

From the moment of your birth, your journey is yours alone. Owing to our complexity as biological organisms in an ever-changing environment, we each see things differently. No one else hears quite the music you hear.

The nursing home tries to turn elders into conforming numbers. Same bedspread, same dinner, same routine. Yet it is well known that people become more diverse, more individual, as they age.

Emotional maturity loosens the conforming chains of youth. We can finally stop trying to fit in, dumbing ourselves down, biting our tongues, and downplaying our talents.

"The greatest thing in the world is know how to belong to oneself."

Michael de Montaigne

The Value of

Mindfulness

"Time and tide wait for

no man."

Geoffrey Chaucer

As birthdays pile up, time becomes increasingly finite. At the age of 100, it's a good bet that days are numbered. At all ages, there is a risk of death, but this is mere probability; in old age, the end looms as a certainty.

What do you do with this knowledge?

Failure to seize moments to right wrongs, follow dreams, or give love can, and does, alter the meaning of your life story.

I know a woman 101 years old who refuses to reconcile with her son after 40 years of estrangement. This might be fully justified. I hope it is, because the opportunity is on the verge of being lost.

I know a woman 55 who looks at her half-written stories with sad regret, wishing she had committed to perfecting her art. At 55, she makes that choice every day.

Time is relative and our perception of it, subjective. We procrastinate as if our intentions, themselves, would write the book, finish the painting, or say, "I'm sorry". But intentions are not actions, and the future will cease.

"Carpe diem, quam

minimum credula postero."

(Seize the day, put little

trust in tomorrow.)

Horace

Become a Connoisseur of Time

Train yourself to taste and smell moments.

Become a sommelier of fine hours to serve others and yourself

Learn the language to describe particularly salient periods of time. Write them down. Savor them.

"Like a proud hometown
parade
Life passed by a smiling,
clapping we,
Too fast. Too beautiful.
Gone."
Mary Lambert Harrington

"A toast to Auld Lang Syne:
to my own midlife crisis at
22, my lost year; to excess,
forgetfulness, failure and
blindness. In many ways,
friends, the best year
of my life."
Chris Stevens (John Corbett),
Northern Exposure

Value a Normal Day

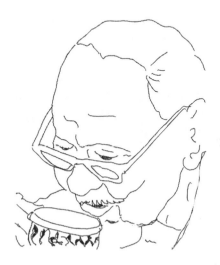

Life seems to be a brimming collection of milestones and accomplishments, full of meaning and emotion. But, in fact, more moments of life are spent in ritualized habits – getting dressed, washing dishes. The daily routine is much disrespected as boring or nonessential. That's a shame because this domestic business of living is the foundation for everything else.

A daily schedule becomes comfortable second nature. It permits a feeling of reassurance that things will proceed as usual. It is a fortress against depression. It is a continual investment in the future – I do laundry so I have something to wear tomorrow.

Importantly, daily routine forms a hedge against memory loss, impaired vision, and reduced mobility. It is easier to find, see and reach things in a familiar world. It is easier to remember who, what, and where you are.

It may be helpful to understand the importance of feeding the cat and sweeping the porch as routine activities that permit your mind the luxury of wandering. As you continuously do little things to invest in an orderly environment and imminent future, you construct an underpinning for the erection of loftier goals.

When elders leave their homes for a nursing facility, they bring their lives with them. But nothing in the heavy, rigid rules of an institution permits carrying on as usual. Lost are the chosen meal times, showering after morning coffee, making dinner, grocery shopping, walking the dog.

The importance of routine becomes clear in the nursing home resident's struggle to maintain it: an afternoon stroll becomes pacing the halls. Most complaints in the nursing home stem from disruptions of these daily routines. This is not nit-picking or self-pity; this is evidence that daily activities provide meaning to our lives.

The Value of

Acceptance

Life is not a box of chocolates.

Life is a deadly struggle for mastery and meaning. Pain, grievous loss, failure, and risk abound, as do lasting love, spontaneous laughter, and moments of deep satisfaction.

Acceptance creates wisdom.

"It is not the strongest or the most intelligent who will survive but those who can best manage change."

Leon C. Megginson

Memento Mori

"Good health is merely the slowest possible rate at which one can die."

Unknown

The technological achievement of doubling the average human life span is radical and exciting, but it has not made us immortal. Every single one of us is still going to die.

Ironically, our longer lives have made us more anxious and obsessed with mortality. Consider that Americans spend more than $400 billion annually for medications. We go to doctors, hospitals, and walk-in clinics at an alarming rate.

Rather than focus our energy and money on making the most of our bonus years, we spend it trying to prolong them.

Isn't this like the Las Vegas slots player who won a million dollars and then put it all back in, trying to win more?

The average number of pills for a nursing home resident is 12 per day. There's Coumadin for blood clots, Inderal for heart attacks, Humalog for blood sugar, antibiotics for infections, flu shots, and Prozac for depression. To prevent choking, food is pureed to smithereens, and served with gelatinous, thickened liquids. There are pacemakers, feeding tubes, IV's and respirators. There are bedside fall mats, obstructive cushions, and "mobility alarms" that scream every time the elder tries to stand up.

There is an entire, thriving industry around prolonging life, and only a sliver of one around choosing wisely.

"Medical science has given us remarkable power to push against these (biological) limits, and the potential value of this power was a central reason I became a doctor. But again and again, I have seen the damage we in medicine do when we fail to acknowledge that such power is finite and always will be."

Atul Gawande

The End of Life

"A man who procrastinates in his choosing will inevitably have his choice made for him by circumstance."

Hunter S. Thompson

It is tempting to think about dying a little bit like winning the lottery: if it ever happens, it will probably be a surprise. But for the long-lived, death is rarely an unexpected visitor. Over 40% of those over 65 die in a hospital, and 30% in nursing homes or hospice facilities. Many more who die at home do so with end-of-life care.

The odds are very good that someone will be making medical decisions at the end of your life. If you do not do it in advance, it may be left to grieving family members or strangers employed at medical facilities. The kindest thing you can do for them is to define your beliefs about how and under what circumstances you want to let go. Then, empower someone you trust to carry out your wishes in case you cannot.

Caution: executing the form to make end-of-life decisions is simple. Commonly, though, people then find 100 excuses to avoid finishing it. Face down this psychological resistance. If you wait too long, there will be no partial credit for planning to one day complete that form.

It is not just for others that you must assume responsibility for end-of-life decisions. It is essential to your own acceptance of mortality. Throwing off the burden of futile denial will free you in your quest to enjoy a long life.

Peace of mind is not a gift, it is the result of practice. Talking openly and calmly about death is such practice. There are as many different ways to die as there are people who do it, but a common thread in those who die peacefully, without regret, with a true, poignant love for life, is acceptance.

The Value of

Action

The foolishness of youth flings away hours in melodrama and conflict without a thought to it. Then, upon aging, regret recalls the hours, days, and months, seeing for the first time how they might have been wisely invested.

It all matters. Choose to live your days in ways that have meaning to you.

"Knowing is not enough; we must apply. Willing is not enough; we must do."

Johann Wolfgang von Goethe

Root out Ageism

Are you uncomfortable around the aged? Do you yell to communicate? Drum impatient fingers on countertops? Do you try to move them along quickly so you can get on to your busy day?

You are creating society's attitude towards long life; it will be as supportive, gracious, and well-mannered as you make it. Respect these people who stand in shoes you may one day fill.

The nursing home threatens to make elders live out of sight and out of mind, but that is a dangerous practice to accept.

Is that how you will want to live?

"What was the hardest prejudice to let go of? A prejudice against myself— my own future, older self— as inferior to my younger self. That's the linchpin of age denial."

Ashton Applewhite

Lift Your Eyes

A golf pro once told me this trick to perfecting the game: swing through the ball. Mentally halting the action at the point of impact disrupts the all-important flow.

A hospice volunteer once told me this trick: until you die, you're alive. Mentally, living and dying are exactly the same.

"Wherever you go, go with all your heart."

Confucius

We are a species awash in internal activities: dialogues, daydreams, replayed memories. As long as you are alive, that stream of consciousness will flow like a narrow creek in the spring flood. The trick is to continue feeding into it things that look ahead – dreams, plans and fantasies about the future.

Our whole lives are spent dreaming of uncertain futures that may or may not come to be.

In the nursing home, some people have given up on life. They have laid down their arms as if there is nothing left to fight for. The world has withdrawn the external motivations for purposeful action, and they have not lived in such a way as to build internal ones.

Find ways to become more open, more useful, more creative, rather than narrowing down.

Do not stop at the point of impact.

You have been swinging through the ball your whole life.

Find Your Passion

"The opposite of fear is love – love of the challenge, love of the work, the pure, joyous passion to take a shot at our dream and see if we can pull it off."

Steven Pressfield

"Life is short", we always say. "There's never enough time."

Time for what?

The top regrets of people who live in nursing homes:

Not pursuing their dreams
Neglecting relationships
Conforming
Taking it all too seriously

Middle age is the time of greatest unhappiness, according to researchers. They attribute this to the hounding pressures that consume our days: making a living, raising children and young adults, assisting our parents. Most people find that their own dreams become like strangers during these years.

Preparing to age successfully demands a certain ruthlessness in making way for your passions. Keep your dreams alive in whatever ways you can: studying, watching documentaries, reading and talking about the things you love. You may get yourself fired up enough to hit the ground running when retirement finally arrives.

Imagine you have been granted a wish for extra time in which to gain mastery.

CARRY IT FORWARD

It is hard to even imagine the love-children of the 1960's submitting to life in nursing homes. This is not a generation who will blindly accept the status quo. This is the protest, counter-culture generation with practice in leading social change.

Thinking about long life and how you will want to age is a heavy thing but today's pre-elders are not afraid of stepping up. Activism is a hallmark feature of the now-boomer generation. Youthful idealism aside, the history of communes reminds us that people can seek ways to live together in nurturing groups.

If we can begin to grow a fondness for our older selves, friends, and families, and to take pride in the achievement, then we will see the symbolic pain of the nursing home become unlinked from our beliefs about long life.

The times are changing and nursing homes are doomed. There are individuals around the world developing better models for elder support. Small-scale homes with family-like care, cooperative housing, community support centers and "dementia villages" are just a few of the new approaches. These alternatives arise from pre-elders lifting their eyes to the future and envisioning something better.

There will come a day, not far off, when we will understand the depth of how broken this nursing home model has been, and how drastically a mere shift in perspective can improve long lives.

Do you ever have a breakthrough insight and then think, "This knowledge would have been useful 20 years ago?" Imagine what you will know in 20 more years. Imagine what you will discover if you work at it.

Two hundred years ago, age denial might have served a purpose. Now, it only holds us back. I see independent elders every day who keep good spirits and remain committed to life. But they were not prepared for what the later years might bring.

Creating a foundation for yourself, making thoughtful decisions for the future, practicing the skills you will need to grow strong – these actions are game changers.

We have been granted an abundance in so many ways. It would be a shame to let it all slip away from sheer neglect.

Live long years and find the treasures they hold.

Look to the future with every intention of having fun.

NOTES

No depiction – pictorial or literary – is based on any individual nursing home patient, and no names or identifying details are those of actual persons.

All illustrations are by the author, and are based on images and memories of the author's beloved family members and friends.

Quoted Works

Applewhite, Ashton. *This Chair Rocks: A Manifesto Against Ageism.* (Networked Books; 2016)

Chaucer, Geoffrey. *The Canterbury Tales.* (London: Penguin, 2003, transl. published 1951)

Emerson, Ralph Waldo. *Self-Reliance and Other Essays.* (New York: Nelson & Sons, 1841; reprinted New York: Dover, 1993)

Fuller, R. Buckminster. As quoted in *Beyond Civilization : Humanity's Next Great Adventure* (New York: Three Rivers Press, 1999), by Daniel Quinn

Gawande, Atul. *Being Mortal: Medicine and What Matters in the End.* (New York: Metropolitan Books, 2014)

Goethe, Johann Wolfgang von; translated by Saunders, T. Bailey. *The Maxims and Reflections of Goethe.* (New York: MacMillan and Co., 1906)

Harrington, Mary Lambert. *Haiku at 2 A.M.* (2011)

Horace. *Odes: Book 1.* (Rome: about 23 B.C.)

Megginson, Leon C. Quotation from a speech presented to the Southwestern Social Science Association, 1963

Montaigne, Michael de. *The Complete Works of Montaigne*. (Stanford: Stanford Univ. P., orig. printing 1958)

Northern Exposure, "Jaws of Life". Season 3, Episode 66, Oct. 4, 1993. Dir. Jim Charleston, Writers Mitchell Burgess and Robin Green

Pressfield, Steven. *Do the Work! Overcome Resistance and get out of your own way*. (Do You Zoom, Inc., 2011)

Schweitzer, Albert. *Out of My Life and Thought*. (Baltimore: Johns Hopkins University P, 1998; orig. published 1933 Henry Holt & Co.)

Thompson, Hunter S. *The Proud Highway: Saga of a Desperate Southern Gentleman*. (New York: Villard, 1997)

Twain, Mark. *Following the Equator*. (Hartford: American Publishing Co., 1897)

Made in the USA
San Bernardino, CA
21 April 2017